# Aria's
# Crown

# Aria's
# Crown

BETTINITA HARRIS

# DEDICATION

I dedicate this book to my parents – Marvin L. and Jewelene Harris – who taught me love of self, love of family and love of God.

# ACKNOWLEDGMENTS

I would like to acknowledge my husband, Nathan, who walked with me on this journey; my family, who encouraged me at every step of the journey; my talented illustrator, who provided what I needed on this journey and Pam, whose words provided the foundation upon which I built my definiteness of purpose.

Aria runs through the front door. Hangs up her backpack. Kicks off her shoes. And plops down on a chair at the kitchen table.

Queen can tell something isn't quite right. After school, Aria usually arrives home like a whirlwind.

She's chattering about what she learned in science, bragging about her antics on the tire swing or laughing so hard it's difficult for her to re-tell a joke she heard during lunch.

"My goodness, child!" says Queen, as she hands her granddaughter a peanut butter sandwich – no jelly and no crust. "How was your day at school? What creative activities did Miss Carmichael dream up for you today?"

Aria's shoulders sag as she lets out a deep sigh. She bites into her sandwich and gulps it down with cold chocolate milk.

"Tomorrow is Grandparents' Day, and I had to make a card for you and Pa," Aria says. "I worked really hard on the card. I drew a butterfly, a ladybug and a unicorn."

Queen is caught by surprise. But this is the best kind of surprise.

Aria shows Queen the card for Grandparents' Day and tries to act excited about the activities her school will have tomorrow. She wants Queen and Pa to be proud of her, but something is bothering her.

Queen is so happy about the card and Grandparents' Day that Aria isn't sure what to say. She doesn't want to spoil the special day.

"Ahh ... Grandparents' Day. It's the day I have waited for since you were born five years ago. I can't wait to see your classroom and see all the work you've done," Queen says.

"Now, you will discover the greatness that is placed inside of you."

Aria knows how important education is to Queen because she talks about it all the time. She tells stories about growing up and how her father worked two jobs while he went to college, but still found time to take care of his family.

Queen likes to talk about her first two years in college being the best, because she was going to the same college as her father. Tuesdays and Thursdays were the most fun, because they would eat lunch together at the cafeteria.

It was during those lunchtimes that Queen's father would tell stories about the importance of doing your best in school. Everyone has the power to give his best effort in school. No one can stop you from learning.

And when you do your best, good things can happen. That's the message Queen often delivers to Aria.

"Aria, you can become anything you want," says Queen, who is already gathering a list in her head. "A scientist who finds a cure for a terrible disease. A Supreme Court justice. Even President of the United States.

"Limitless possibilities, that's what you have, Aria. Limitless possibilities."

But Aria isn't sure she believes what Queen is saying. Something that happened in class today made her sad.

Aria takes another swig of milk, before burying her face in her hands. "Today in circle time, Miss Carmichael asked what we called our grandparents.

"Some kids call their grandmothers Grandma, Mom-Mom, Nana, Gigi and Grammie. When my turn came, I said I call you Queen. The kids all laughed at me and said you were not a queen."

"And what do you say, Aria?"

The little girl shrugs. "Well, you don't live in a castle. You don't sit on a throne. And I've never seen you wear a crown. Are you a queen?"

Queen twirls her salt-and-pepper locs, as she often does when deep in thought.

"Let's get on the laptop and Google the definition of queen."

Off the pair goes to the study. Queen settles in behind the cherry desk and Aria scrambles to sit on her grandmother's lap as she opens the computer.

"Hmmm, let's see. It says: A queen is a woman who rules."

"What does 'rules' mean?" Aria asks.

"It means to be in charge."

"That's you, Queen! You are in charge. What else does it say?"

"It says a queen is a woman who is powerful within a family."

"That's you, Queen! You are a woman and you are powerful in our family. You ARE a queen."

Aria squeals. Jumps over the desk and soars into a cartwheel. Queen isn't fond of Aria doing gymnastic moves in the house, but today she makes an exception.

## Colored Girls

I created Colored Girl Wisdom, LLC, a multimedia company, to encourage, inspire and empower black girls to embrace who they are in a world where we are invisible.
But black women also can benefit from these life lessons.
My hope is that girls and women around the world of similar hues will learn -- sooner than I did -- that their crowns are already bought and paid for.

"Let me explain why I chose the name," the grandmother says. "I wanted you to know you were connected to something greater than yourself. Never underestimate the greatness that has been placed inside of you."

Aria seems confused. "So you *are* a *real* queen?"

"Some people may not believe that I am a queen. But it doesn't matter. What matters most is what I think and what I believe about myself."

"What do you mean, Queen?" Aria asks.

"People will sometimes put a label on you. Labels can be good. But some labels can be limiting," Queen says. "You can accept labels people give you. Or you can decide who you are and choose your own label."

"So, that's what you did, Queen?"

"Yes. You see, Aria, if I decide my name, I also can define what that name means," Queen says. "I take care of my family.

"I help people in my community. I stand up for what I believe. And I try to do the right thing.

"To me, that's what a queen is. You may not see my crown, but it's there – bought and paid for," continues the grandmother, straightening the invisible jeweled crown on her head.

Aria likes the idea of wearing a crown. She also likes the idea of deciding who she is.

It sounds cool to be connected to something greater. And that gives Aria an idea.

"How about this, Queen? How about we put our names together? That way we will always be connected," Aria says.

Queen twists her locs again. "Hmmm," she thinks to herself. "How can we make this work? Aria Queen? Queen Aria?"

And then it hits her: "How about Queen-A? Queen for me. And 'A' for Aria."

"That's it!" Aria yells. "Queeeen-A! Queeeen-A! Queeeen-A!

"You will always be my Queen-A."

Coming soon...Other titles in the
Sisters for Life, Best Friends Forever series

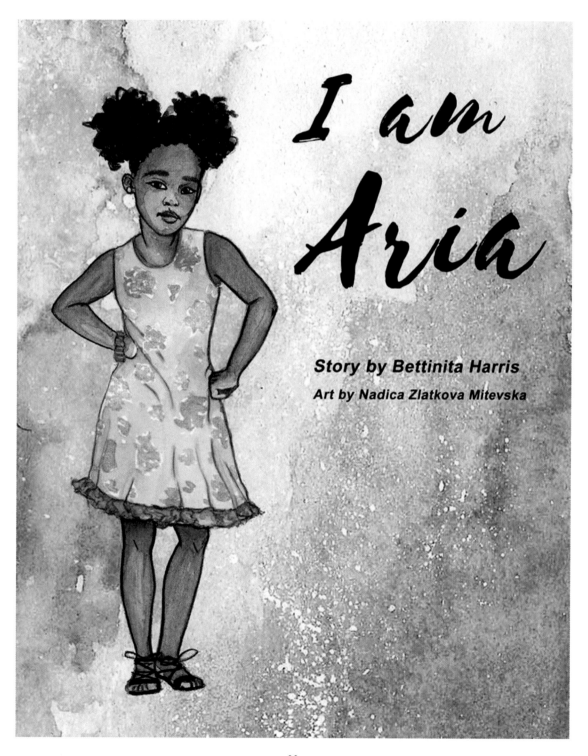

# I am Aria

**Story by Bettinita Harris**

*Art by Nadica Zlatkova Mitevska*

Coming soon...Other titles in the
Sisters for Life, Best Friends Forever series

ARIA'S ROCKIN' POUFS

*Story by Bettinita Harris*
*Art by Nadica Zlatkova Mitevska*

Coming soon...Other titles in the
Sisters for Life, Best Friends Forever series

# ABOUT THE AUTHOR

**B**ettinita Harris' award-winning journalism career has spanned more than 20 years at some of the nation's most prestigious newspapers, including The Philadelphia Inquirer, the Star Tribune in Minneapolis and The Tampa Tribune. The hallmark of her work as a reporter and editor has been the rare ability to capture the souls of her subjects and share this intimate insight with the world.

She was a pioneer in bringing to light the unseen ramifications of the AIDS crisis in the United States, becoming the nation's first journalist to tell the story of the three young Ray brothers in Florida.

After contracting HIV from infected blood transfusions used to treat their hemophilia, the boys and their family endured horrific treatment. They were expelled from public school due to hysteria over their condition and ostracized by the community.

Bettinita documented the family's struggle every step of the way in The Tampa Tribune, including their victory in federal court that returned the boys to public school and the arson of their home a week later. The family's story became front-page news across the country, and their resulting activism in educating the public and dispelling myths about AIDS is considered a seminal event in the history of the disease and its repercussions in America.

Bettinita's work as an editor includes guiding reporters on numerous stories that upended the status quo, exposed institutional wrongdoing or gave voice to heart-rending tales of suffering and struggle.

An investigation by The Commercial Appeal uncovered 80 convicted felons working in the public school system of Memphis, Tenn., leading the administration to remove the employees and change its hiring practices.

Devastating flooding in Grand Forks, N.D., resulted in Bettinita leading a team of reporters and photographers to produce special reports that vividly portrayed the damage to a small, tight-knit community and spawned an outpouring of donations from readers of the Star Tribune.

A race riot in Shreveport, La., was the impetus for the Shreveport Times' award-winning series of stories examining the roots of conflict in the community and prompting several public forums involving nationally renowned experts in race relations.

Bettinita's knack for finding stories that resonate led The Philadelphia Inquirer to choose her as the architect for the newspaper's most ambitious undertaking in decades, the introduction of a daily publication devoted to its prized target market of Chester County, Pa., one of the nation's most affluent counties.

She orchestrated the project to tremendous success, generating 10 percent daily circulation growth at a time when newspapers across the country were losing readers in droves. The project attracted national publicity from the media.

Bettinita's experience with publishing includes serving as lead editor for "I Am A Man," a pictorial history chronicling Dr. Martin Luther King Jr.'s involvement in the Memphis sanitation workers strike that precipitated his 1968 assassination. She worked with numerous leaders of the civil rights movement to collect their remembrances of the event and preserve a watershed moment of U.S. history.

Another career highlight was her profile of Linda Brown Smith, a key figure in the landmark Brown v. Board of Education of Topeka, Kan., ruling by the U.S. Supreme Court that declared segregation in public schools unconstitutional.

Bettinita lives in West Chester, Pa., and when she is not writing children's books works as a substitute teacher in various school districts in Chester County and Delaware County. She is married and has two children and two granddaughters.

# www.coloredgirlwisdom.com

Subscribe to my website and receive
an original water color poster
called "ENCOURAGE."

Made in the USA
Monee, IL
09 June 2020